Do You Know Which Ones Will Grow?

Description

Learners explore the phenomenon that some things grow (like people, cats, and snakes) and other things do not grow (like chairs, hats, and cakes). They learn the difference between living and nonliving things and what living things need to survive.

Alignment With the *Next Generation Science Standards*

Performance Expectation		
K-LS1-1: Use observations to describe patterns of what plants and animals (including humans) need to survive.		
Science and Engineering Practices	**Disciplinary Core Idea**	**Crosscutting Concept**
Analyzing and Interpreting Data Use observations (firsthand or from media) to describe patterns and/or relationships in the natural and designed world(s) in order to answer scientific questions and solve problems. Engaging in Argument From Evidence Construct an argument with evidence to support a claim.	LS1.C: Organization for Matter and Energy Flow in Organisms All animals need food in order to live and grow. They obtain their food from plants or from other animals. Plants need water and light to live and grow.	Patterns Patterns in the natural and human-designed world can be observed, used to describe phenomena, and used as evidence.

Note: The activities in this lesson will help students move toward the performance expectation listed, which is the goal after multiple activities. However, the activities will not by themselves be sufficient to reach the performance expectation.

Featured Picture Books

TITLE: ***Do You Know Which Ones Will Grow?***
AUTHOR: **Susan A. Shea**
ILLUSTRATOR: **Tom Slaughter**
PUBLISHER: **Blue Apple Books**
YEAR: **2011**
GENRE: **Non-Narrative Information**
SUMMARY: *Rhyming text and fun lift-the-flap illustrations ask the reader which things will grow, such as "If a duckling grows and becomes a duck, can a car grow and become a … truck?"*

TITLE: ***What's Alive?***
AUTHOR: **Kathleen Weidner Zoehfeld**
ILLUSTRATOR: **Nadine Bernard Westcott**
PUBLISHER: **HarperCollins**
YEAR: **1995**
GENRE: **Narrative Information**
SUMMARY: *From the Let's-Read-and-Find-Out Science series, this book introduces students to the differences between living and nonliving things.*

Time Needed

This lesson will take several class periods. Suggested scheduling is as follows:

Session 1: Engage with Open Sort, Do You Know Which Ones Will Grow? Read-Aloud, and Closed Sort, and Explore with Things That Grow Indoors and Outdoors

Session 2: Explain with What's Alive? Read-Aloud

Session 3: Elaborate with Looking for Living and Nonliving Things

Session 4: Evaluate with Is It Alive? Lift-the-Flap Booklet

Materials

For Open Sort and Closed Sort (per pair)

• Do You Know Which Ones Will Grow? Picture Cards (1 precut set)

For Things That Grow Indoors and Outdoors (per student)

• Clipboard

For Looking for Living and Nonliving Things

• Hand lens (per student)
• Clipboard (per student)
• Hula-Hoop or string to make a circle (per group of 3–4 students)

- Selection of nonliving things (e.g., balls, toys, and rocks) to place in the Hula-Hoop or string circle (per group of 3–4 students)

For Is It Alive? Lift-the-Flap Booklet (per student)

- Magazines
- Scissors
- Markers or crayons
- Glue

Note: The explore and elaborate phases of this lesson require an outdoor area.

For STEM Everywhere (per student)

- Lima bean seed
- Small cup and soil in zipper bag

Student Pages

- Things That Grow Booklet
- Looking for Living and Nonliving Things
- Is It Alive? Lift-the-Flap Booklet
- STEM Everywhere

Background for Teachers

The difference between living and nonliving things is an essential concept for elementary students to understand. It may seem like a simple concept, but it can be tricky for young children. Some commonly agreed-upon criteria are that living things grow, change, reproduce, and have certain needs. However, many nonliving things that children encounter might appear to have one or more of these qualities. A Framework for K–12 Science Education suggests that students learn at an early age that living things have needs that must be met for them to survive. Animals need air, water, and food. Plants need air, water, and light. They do not need to eat food because they make their own. Many students have the misconception that fertilizer is the same as food. They may even have seen fertilizer at the store or at home that is labeled "plant food." It is important for students to understand that fertilizer contains nutrients that help a plant stay healthy (keep cells functioning properly), but it does not contain food.

The main difference between plants' and animals' needs is that plants do not eat food to live and survive. They make their own food from air and water with energy from sunlight, in a process called photosynthesis. The process of photosynthesis likely is too complex for very young children to understand. If students learn that plants need water and sunlight to live and survive, that is sufficient to build the foundation for later understanding of the complex process that plants use to make their own food.

Note: There are a few plants, such as Venus flytraps and pitcher plants, that trap and absorb nutrients from insects. Students may bring these up during the lesson. If so, you can explain that these plants still make their own food, but will "eat" insects to get nutrients that are not available in their environments.

Learning Progressions

Below are the DCI grade band endpoints for grades K–2 and 3–5. These are provided to show how student understanding of the DCI in this lesson will progress in future grade levels.

DCI	Grades K–2	Grades 3–5
LS1.C: Organization for Matter and Energy Flow in Organisms	• All animals need food in order to live and grow. They obtain their food from plants or from other animals. Plants need water and light to live and grow.	• Food provides animals with the materials they need for body repair and growth and the energy they need to maintain body warmth and for motion. • Plants acquire their material for growth chiefly from air and water.

Source: Willard, T., ed. 2015. The NSTA quick-reference guide to the NGSS: Elementary school. Arlington, VA: NSTA Press.

engage

Do You Know Which Ones Will Grow?

Open Sort

Give each pair of students a set of picture cards and ask them to look at each picture and come up with a way of sorting them into groups. If students have not had experience with sorting, you may want to do this as a class. As they are sorting the cards, ask

? What do all of the things in this group (choose one group) have in common?

? How is this thing (pick up a card not in the group) different from the others in the group?

? What other ways could you sort the cards?

When they have finished sorting, have pairs guess how other pairs nearby sorted the pictures by looking at their groups. Discuss the different ways of sorting the pictures and explain that at this point there was no right or wrong way to sort.

Do You Know Which Ones Will Grow? Read-Aloud

Connecting to the Common Core
Reading: Literature
KEY IDEAS AND DETAILS: K.1

Inferring

Show students the cover of Do You Know Which Ones Will Grow? and introduce the author and illustrator. Tell students to listen and watch for the items from their cards as they appear in the book. Read aloud the first few pages to give students a feel for the pattern and rhyme; then, ask students to infer from the illustrations and the text what is under each flap. For example, after reading, "If a kit grows and becomes a fox, can a watch grow and become …" ask students to predict what is under the flap. Then open the flap to reveal a clock.

Closed Sort

After reading, ask students to sort their cards into two groups: Grows and Does Not Grow. Have students look at the Grows group of cards. Say, "All of the things in this group of cards grow" and ask

? How else are the things in this group the same? (They are animals, they move, they have parents, and they are alive.)

? What do you think the things in this group need to grow? (Answers will vary, but may include air, food, and water.)

? How can you tell if something is alive? (Answers will vary, but may include it moves, it grows, and it eats.)

? What questions do you have about the things in the Grows group? (Answers will vary.)

explore

Things That Grow Indoors and Outdoors

Tell students that you are going to look for more things that grow. Give each student a copy of the Things That Grow booklet and a clipboard. Tell them that on the left-hand page they are going to make a list of things in the classroom that grow. They can record this list in words or pictures. Allow them time to walk around the room quietly with their clipboards, booklets, and pencils and look for things that grow. If your classroom does not contain any plants or animals, they likely will not have much to list—except themselves! Bring students back together and have them share some of the items on their lists.

Next, tell students that you are going to do the same exercise, but this time they will be looking for things that grow outdoors and will record their list on the right-hand page. Allow them time to walk around an area outdoors with their clipboards, booklets, and pencils and look for things that grow. Then bring students back together and have them share some of the items on their lists.

SAFETY

- Students should wear closed-toe shoes or sneakers, long pants, long-sleeve shirts, hats, sunglasses, sunscreen, and safety glasses or goggles when working outdoors.

- Caution students to watch out for ticks, mosquitoes, stinging insects, and other potentially hazardous insects when working outdoors.

- Caution students against poisonous plants such as poison ivy or poison sumac when working outdoors.

- Check with the school nurse regarding student medical issues (e.g., allergies to bee stings) and how to deal with them.

- Find out whether the outdoor area have been treated with pesticides, fungicides, or any other toxins, and avoid any such areas.

- Bring some form of communication, such as a cell phone or two-way radio, in case of emergencies.

- Inform parents in writing of a planned field trip, any potential hazards, and the safety precautions being taken.

- Have students wash their hands with soap and water upon completing the activity.

LOOKING FOR THINGS THAT GROW OUTDOORS

Ask

? What kinds of things did you find inside that grow? (people, plants, bugs)

? What kinds of things did you find outside that grow? (people, plants, bugs, grass, trees, birds, squirrels, etc.)

? How are these things that grow like the things in our Grows cards from the card sort? (They are alive.)

? Were there more kinds of living things indoors or outdoors? (outdoors) Why?

> **SEP: Analyzing and Interpreting Data**
> Use observations to describe patterns in the natural world.

Choose two animals students saw that are different from the animals in the card sort. Ask

? What does [the first animal] need to grow?

? What about [the second animal]?

? Do you think all animals need these things to grow?

Next, choose two plants students saw inside or outside, and ask

? What does [the first plant] need to grow?

? What about [the second plant]?

? Do you think we need separate lists for what animals need to grow and what plants need to grow?

explain

What's Alive? Read-Aloud

Connecting to the Common Core
Reading: Informational Text
KEY IDEAS AND DETAILS: K.1

Determining Importance

Tell students that you have a book that will help them learn more about how to tell if something is alive and what living things need in order to grow. Show students the cover of *What's Alive?* by Kathleen Weidner Zoehfeld. Tell students that as you read the book aloud, you would like them to listen for all of the ways that living things are alike. Read the book aloud, pausing periodically to point out the ways in which living things are alike:

- Living things need food.
- Living things need water.
- Living things need air.
- Living things grow.
- Living things move.

Monitoring Comprehension

After reading page 16, which says that plants "need water, air, and food. And they can move and grow," pause to model how good readers monitors their comprehension by verbalizing your "inner conversation." You might say, "Wow, that sounds important, so I am going to reread it." After rereading that sentence, ask

? Do plants eat food the way animals do? (no)

? Then how do they get food? (Answers will vary.)

? Do they move around the way animals do? (No, they do not run, jump, or fly.)

? Then how do they move? (Answers will vary.)

After reading page 20, discuss how plants get food (they make it) and how they move (grow and bend).

Explain to students another trait that all living things have is the ability to reproduce, or make more of themselves. For example, the cat on pages 12 and 13 had kittens, the bird on pages 14 and 15 hatched from an egg its mother laid, and the trees and flowers on page 18 made seeds that will grow into new trees and flowers. Then, read the rest of the book aloud.

National Science Teaching Association

 Questioning

Ask

? What do we call things that are not living things? (nonliving things)

? What were some examples of nonliving things from the book? (stone, tricycle, book, doll, etc.)

? What if you find a brown, dried-up plant or an insect that is not moving anymore? Is it living or nonliving? (They are living things that have died.)

? What do plants and animals have in common? (They are living; they grow; they change; they reproduce; and they need air, food, and water.)

? How are plants and animals different? (Plants are often green, they don't move around like animals, and many plants make seeds instead of laying eggs or having babies.)

> **CCC: Patterns**
> Patterns in the natural world can be observed.

Tell students that plants and animals are also very different in the way that they get food. Explain that animals eat plants or other animals to get energy, but plants make their food out of water and air with energy from the Sun. So plants do not "eat" anything. A common misconception with young students is that plants take in food from the soil. This is incorrect. Explain to students that plants can get nutrients from the soil or fertilizer, but this is not food. It is similar to how people take vitamins. They give us nutrients, but we could not survive on vitamins alone because they are not food.

Connecting to the Common Core
Reading: Informational Text
KEY IDEAS AND DETAILS: K.2

Determining Importance

Ask

? If a friend asked you what this book is about, what would you tell them? In other words, what is the main topic of the book? (Have students turn and talk. Students should recognize that the main topic of the book is how to tell what's alive and what's not.)

Explain to students that quite often, the more we learn in science, the more questions we have. Then, ask

? After reading the book, what do you wonder about living things?

elaborate

Looking for Living and Nonliving Things

Ahead of time, set up a Hula-Hoop or circle of string for each group of three or four students in a grassy area outdoors. In each Hula-Hoop or circle, be sure there are examples of several living things (e.g., grass, insects, flowers) and nonliving things (e.g., ball, toy, rock). Give each student a copy of the Looking for Living and Nonliving Things student page, a clipboard, and a hand lens. Divide students into groups and assign each group a hooped area (circle) to quietly explore. Have students draw and label what they see in their circle and make a list of all the living things and all the nonliving things they see in the circle. Visit groups as they are working and ask them to point out some living and nonliving things to you. Encourage them to use their hand lenses to look very closely. Ask guiding questions, such as

? How do you know that is living/nonliving?

? Does it need air, food, and water?

? Does it grow?

? Does it move?

Students may find some dried twigs, brown leaves, or dead insects in their circles. Explain to

LOOKING FOR LIVING AND NONLIVING THINGS

them that these items do not fit into either category on the student page. They are in another category called once-living things.

After returning to the classroom, have students share their drawings and their lists of living and nonliving things.

evaluate

Is It Alive? Lift-the-Flap Booklet

Connecting to the Common Core
Writing
RESEARCH TO BUILD AND PRESENT KNOWLEDGE: K.8

CCC: Patterns
Patterns in the natural world can be used as evidence.

Writing

Tell students that they are going to help create an "Is It Alive?" bulletin board. Revisit the book Do You Know Which Ones Will Grow? and remind students how the flaps in the book worked. Give each student the Is It Alive? lift-the-flap booklet student page folded on the dotted line, some magazines, markers or crayons, glue, and scissors.

SAFETY
Tell students to use caution in working with sharp items like scissors, because they can cut or puncture skin.

SEP: Engaging in Argument From Evidence
Construct an argument with evidence to support a claim.

Tell students that they are going to be creating something similar to the flaps in the book. On the outside of their booklet, they will glue

LIFT-THE-FLAP BOOKLET

or draw a picture of something living or non-living. On the inside of the booklet they will write "yes" if the thing is living and "no" if it is not. They will also answer the question, "How do you know?" This activity gives students the opportunity to make a claim and support it with evidence. Possible answers are as follows:

Nonliving

- No. It does not need food, air, or water.
- No. It does not move or grow.
- No. It does not make more of itself (reproduce).
- No. It cannot die.

Living

- Yes. It needs air, food, and water.
- Yes. It grows and moves.

- Yes. It can make more of itself (reproduce).
- Yes. It can die.

Evaluate student understanding by checking that they correctly identified the picture as living or nonliving and assessing their answer to the question "How do you know?" inside the booklet. Display all of the booklets on a bulletin board with the title "Is It Alive?" Invite students to look at their classmates' booklets and decide if each thing is alive or not and check their answers under the flaps.

After the lesson, prompt students to think about their own learning. Ask

? How have your ideas changed about living things?

? What do you know now that you didn't know before?

? How can you use what you've learned?

? What are you still wondering about living things?

STEM Everywhere

Give students the STEM Everywhere student page as a way to involve their families and extend their learning. They can do this activity with an adult helper and share their results with the class. If students do not have access to the internet at home, you may choose to show the video at school.

Opportunities for Differentiated Instruction

This box lists questions and challenges related to the lesson that students may select to research, investigate, or innovate. Students may also use the questions as examples to help them generate their own questions. These questions can help you move your students from the teacher-directed investigation to engaging in the science and engineering practices in a more student-directed format.

Extra Support

For students who are struggling to meet the lesson objectives, provide a question and guide them in the process of collecting research or helping them design procedures or solutions.

Extensions

For students with high interest or who have already met the lesson objectives, have them choose a question (or pose their own question), conduct their own research, and design their own procedures or solutions.

Continued

Opportunities for Differentiated Instruction (*continued*)

After selecting one of the questions in this box or formulating their own questions, students can individually or collaboratively make predictions, design investigations or surveys to test their predictions, collect evidence, devise explanations, design solutions, or examine related resources. They can communicate their findings through a science notebook, at a poster session or gallery walk, or by producing a media project.

Research

Have students brainstorm researchable questions:

? How are living things classified, or sorted, by scientists?

? What other living things are there besides plants and animals?

? How do desert plants get water?

Investigate

Have students brainstorm testable questions to be solved through science or math:

? Does a seed need sunlight to sprout?

? Do roots always grow down?

? What happens when you water a plant too much?

Innovate

Have students brainstorm problems to be solved through engineering:

? Can you design a way to water a plant when you are on vacation?

? Can you design a container to grow a plant out of used materials?

? Can you design a habitat that will meet the needs of a classroom pet?

More Books to Read

Kalman, B. 2008. *Is it a living thing?* New York: Crabtree.
Summary: This book details the characteristics of living things, including that they are made of cells and have life cycles. It includes captions and an index.

Lindeen, C. 2008. *Living and nonliving.* Mankato, MN: Capstone Press.
Summary: Simple text and photographs introduce young students to the differences between living and nonliving things.

Rissman, R. 2009. *Is it living or nonliving?* Chicago: Heinemann Library.
Summary: This Acorn Read-Aloud title explains how to tell if something is living. It includes an index, bold-print words, and glossary.

Royston, A. 2008. *Living and nonliving.* Chicago: Heinemann Library.
Summary: This book from the *My World of Science* series describes the difference between living and nonliving things. It includes an index, bold-print words, and glossary.

Silver, D. M. 1997. *One small square: Backyard.* New York: McGraw-Hill.
Summary: This book teaches children that a small square of earth can yield up an endlessly complex and fascinating interaction of plants and animals with their environment, and shows them how to study the area as a scientist would.

Picture Cards

Picture Cards

National Science Teaching Association

Picture Cards

Picture Cards

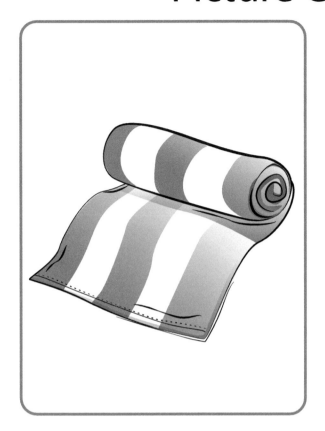

National Science Teaching Association

Picture Cards

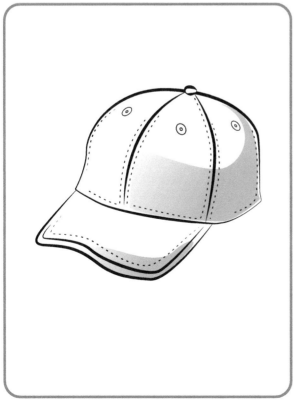

Things That Grow

By _____

Things That Grow

In the Classroom

- -

Things That Grow

Outdoors

Name: _____

Looking for **Living** and **Nonliving Things**

Draw what you see in your circle.

Living _____

_____

Nonliving _____

_____

National Science Teaching Association

- -

_____

(yes or no)

How Do You Know?

_____

_____

_____

_____

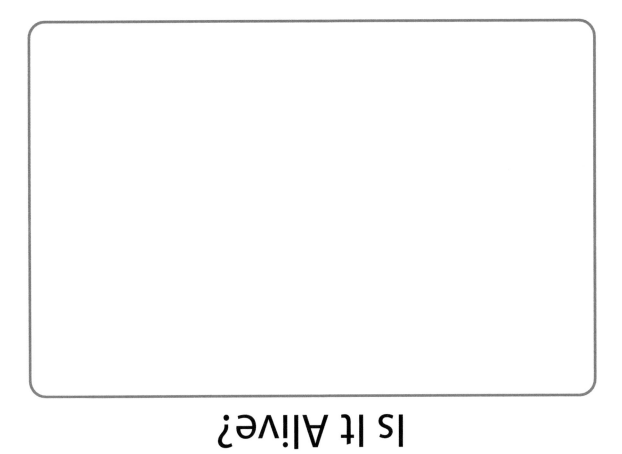

Is It Alive?

Name: _____

STEM Everywhere

Dear Families,

At school, we have been learning about **the needs of living things.** We learned that all animals need food in order to live and grow. They get their food from plants or from other animals. Plants need water and light to live and grow. To find out more, ask your learner the following questions and discuss their answers:

- What did you learn?
- What was your favorite part of the lesson?
- What are you still wondering?

At home, you can watch an episode of *Sid the Science Kid* titled "Growing Plants" and then plant a lima bean seed in a cup of soil. Water it and watch it grow!

 To find the video, scan the QR code, search "Sid the Science Kid: Growing Plants" in your web browser, or go to *https://pbskids. org/video/sid-science-kid/1568868836*.

Draw a picture of yourself giving the seed what it needs to grow.